Young**Writ**

Young Writers 2006 Creative Writing Com

Scotland & Wales

Edited by Heather Killingray

Disclaimer

Young Writers has maintained every effort
to publish stories that will not cause offence.

Any stories, events or activities relating to individuals
should be read as fictional pieces and not construed
as real-life character portrayal.

 Young**Writers**

First published in Great Britain in 2006 by:
Young Writers
Remus House
Coltsfoot Drive
Peterborough
PE2 9JX
Telephone: 01733 890066
Website: www.youngwriters.co.uk

SB ISBN 1 84602 701 2

Foreword

All children love to read and be read to, and what would delight a child more than writing their very own piece that others can read and have read to them?

Young Writers was established in 1991 to promote the written word amongst school children. Now, in 2006, we are still encouraging children to put themselves forward and to challenge their own talents, especially through specifically tailored projects such as our short story challenge promoted through primary schools nationwide.

To ensure the writer was challenged and that the books offer a variety of writing styles and themes we offered pupils the opportunity to write a short story on a theme of their choice. Alternatively they could have used one of the following to inspire their piece; the ini Saga, a story of 50 words or less; the saga has a beginning, middle and end, often with a twist in the tale. Nursery Rhymes Fairy Tales - we suggested the idea of pupils writing a letter to a character such as Fantasy Forest Council writing to the Big Bad Wolf. As well as that inspiration could be drawn from the theme to write a monologue, a spell, to re-tell a fairy tale, change the ending or even mix and match the characters in stories!

Each piece was chosen on the basis of style, technical skill, ability to entertain and flair for writing, and from the many entries we received, we have produced an outstanding 'Small Talk' series of books, with the pieces written by 7-11 year-olds, all illustrating how imaginative today's children can be. Small Talk Scotland Wales is our latest offering which we are sure you will agree is a fantastic collection, not only showcasing the pupils' work, but the school's ability to inspire and let the children's creativity flow.

We hope you continue to enjoy this delightful collection again and again for it is truly inspired and a credit to all who are featured within the following pages.

Contents

Buckstone Primary School, Edinburgh

Cross Inn Primary School, Aberystwyth

Cultercullen Primary School, Ellon

Glyncoed Junior School, Cardiff

Guilsfield CP School, Welshpool

James Duffy 98
Jordan Burns (11) 99
Kayleigh Bidwell (12) 100
Caroline Burns 101
Matthew Kean 102
Mark Shedden (11) 103

Ysgol Bryn Teg, Llanelli
Charlie Margett (9) 104
Bethany Mullen (8) 105
Katie Burton (10) 106
Andrew Lloyd (10) 107

Ysgol Pentreuchaf, Pwllheli
Laura Kenyon (11) 108
Elain Lloyd (10) 109
Sioned Roberts (11) 110
Ceiri Coker (11) 111
Billy Bagilhole (11) 112
Jim Ellis (11) 113
Gethin Roberts (11) 114
Manon Hollywood (11) 115
Rhian Jones (10) 116
Daniel Roberts (11) 117

The Creative Writing

It's Just A Dream

In a long grassed field twenty cows stood. One oddly spotted cow decided to escape.

She met a fat pig called Pog, a squiggly centipede called Tickle and a most unusual dog that goes round in circles then goes *moo!* Then she woke up in the same old grassy field.

Florence Turley (8)
Abermule Community Primary School, Montgomery

Football Match

I was playing football until it was half-time. I dashed in the changing room and had a chat with the team.

It was time to get back on the pitch for the second half, so we started again and the score was one-nil. What a goal!

Jamie Jones (9)
Abermule Community Primary School, Montgomery

The Three Little Bears

Once there were three bears, Daddy Bear, Mummy Bear and Baby Bear and a girl called Goldilocks. She was crying. The bears saw Goldilocks and went to see her. The bears said, 'What is the matter with you?'

She said, 'I haven't got my dog. He ran away.'

'We will find him for you,' said the bears. They found the dog on the doorstep.

'Goldilocks, we have found your dog.'

She said, 'Thank you.'

'You are welcome,' said the bears.

'Why don't you come to my house?' said Goldilocks.

'Yes, we will,' said the bears.

'I have got a cake and tea and some cookies, chocolate and chocolate biscuits,' said Goldilocks.

They all lived happily ever after.

Polly Jefferis (7)
Abermule Community Primary School, Montgomery

The Chase

'It's ready!' said a woman who was called Mrs Broomstick. She pulled a little figure out of the oven, it was a gingerbread man.

All of a sudden he jumped up and said, 'If you want to eat me, you will have to catch me!' and he ran away. On the way he met a little girl. 'What's your name little girl?'

The girl said, 'It's Georgia. Georgia Muffet. *Argh!*'

'What's wrong Georgia?' said the gingerbread man.

'Oh nothing, just my spider trying to scare me again.'

'Do you want to come with me?'

'What for?'

'Mr and Mrs Broomstick are trying to eat me,' said the gingerbread man.

'What! Those people tried to squish my spider.'

They ran and ran and soon they came to a beautiful woodland valley where they lived forever.

Beth Davies
Abermule Community Primary School, Montgomery

Humpty Dumpty

Humpty Dumpty is strong. He has the biggest muscles in Storyland.

Then a gang of gingerbread men came to steal his money. They said, 'Give us your money or we'll make you eat some eggs!' Humpty Dumpty got out his shotgun and he shot the gingerbreads men's leader. His head fell off. He shot all of the other gingerbread men into tiny crumbs and he ate them.

Then ninja gingerbread men came. They got out their ginger guns and then Little Red Riding Hood came. She took cakes out of her basket and threw them into the air like Frisbees. The ninja gingerbread men jumped into the sky trying to catch the cakes.

Unfortunately, when the ninja gingerbread men landed they all got broken. Humpty Dumpty said, 'Oh my goodness! More gingerbread men to eat! I'll get the plates and you get the picnic mat, we are going to have a feast!'

When they finished their picnic, Humpty Dumpty said, there must be a big cloud coming over Storyland. But they were wrong. It was a shadow of the king-sized gingerbread man. They got out a big, big, big pot, they ate through the big gingerbread man's legs and he fell over into the pot and they made ginger tea.

They all lived happily ever after!

Yeah right!

Charlie Sharrock (8)
Abermule Community Primary School, Montgomery

Mini Saga

My legs were like jelly, my heart was pounding, as I came face to face with the biggest monster in school, Billy the Bully. Our hands locked, our elbows gripped the table and everyone shouted, 'Come on!'

I pushed with all my might, soon his hand was on the table ...

Bethany Harding (9)
Abermule Community Primary School, Montgomery

The Pigs

One day three pigs were lost in a field when suddenly a fox came and went to get them. The pigs ran. The chase went on for three hours.

But then the fox ran too fast and crashed into the fence and that was the end of him.

Henry Williams (8)
Abermule Community Primary School, Montgomery

The Flying Pig

Once there was a pig who loved baked beans. When someone put something in the bin he would always check if it was baked beans.

One day someone did put baked beans in the bin. It took him two days to gobble them all up, then he was flying!

Tonicha Trow (8)
Abermule Community Primary School, Montgomery

Mini Pires

I was running to the goal when aliens came and said, 'Score in the other goal.'

'Why?' I said.

'Because you are mini, we are big and if you score you get five goals.'

So I said, 'Rock on,' and did it.

They tricked me and I went home crying.

Ben Hamer   (9)
Abermule Community Primary School, Montgomery

Goldilocks And The Three Bears

One sunny day, there were three bears that went for a walk in the wood. They found a big house. They went and looked in the window and were surprised to see chocolate all over the kitchen table.

'Let's see if the door is open, I want some chocolate!' said Baby Bear. They all went inside. Baby Bear ran to the kitchen and then at last Mummy and Daddy Bear came and ate some too. Then Baby Bear wanted to go to the living room to play with some toys. Baby Bear played with Barbie dolls. She accidentally pulled the Barbie head off, 'It was an accident Mummy,' Baby Bear said.

'It's OK.'

Let's go home, thought Goldilocks' family. They came home after their walk. Suddenly, the door opened, it was Goldilocks' family.

'Run!' said Daddy Bear. Upstairs in the bedroom there was a door going downstairs and out the back door. They went down there. They were free again. Goldilocks noticed the chocolate was gone.

'I will buy some more.'

'Someone has broken my Barbie too!'

'I will buy you one of those too.'

The three bears never came back there again.

Ruby Anthony (9)
Abermule Community Primary School, Montgomery

Mini Saga

There was a horse called Dobbin pulling a plough in a bumpy field. He said, 'Why do I have to do this?'

The farmer said, 'I don't have any money to buy a tractor.'

Dobbin went into his stable. Next thing he knew, he heard *chug, chug, chug, chug.*

Kelly Vaughan (9)
Abermule Community Primary School, Montgomery

The Green Monkey

One day a monkey called James was helping his mate paint a tree green. James laughed as he watched his mate do the funniest thing.

His mate walked towards the tree and slipped on a banana skin landing in a tub of green paint! He then became the green monkey.

Rhian Jones (11)
Abermule Community Primary School, Montgomery

The Zombies

One fine night, two zombies got up to fight. They drew their swords back to back, they turned and walked away from each other, ran back to the other, the swords clanged and pinged.

Suddenly, another zombie came and chopped off their heads and then the zombie went to sleep!

Daniel Jones (11)
Abermule Community Primary School, Montgomery

The Hamster That Wanted To Fly

In a flat above a fish and chip shop lived a hamster that wanted to fly.

Jumbo the hamster had tried to fly before but had never succeeded. Today, he said, 'I will fly,' and so he climbed onto the roof of his cage when …

Leela Davies (10)
Abermule Community Primary School, Montgomery

Lost Dog

First the baby, now the puppy. I don't know what's happening. I took the dog for a walk and this happened.

It started to rain and she turned round, snatched the lead and ran off! We searched for her for three days and eventually found her, she had been run over!

Sarah Woodhouse (11)
Abermule Community Primary School, Montgomery

High School

Today was the first day of high school for Claire.

'Come on Claire, you're going to be late for the bus,' shouted her mum.

Claire plodded down the stairs. 'I don't want to go,' she muttered.

'Go on, you'll have a great time,' said her mum in a calm voice.

Catrin Griffiths (11)
Abermule Community Primary School, Montgomery

Letter To Hansel And Gretel

Dear Hansel and Gretel,

   Great news that you killed the witch. I hope you're having a nice time with your daddy. I'm sorry to hear that your stepmother died. I should think that both of you feel very sick because of that candy house. Is that candy house for sale now the witch has gone? I really would like to live there; I can taste the sugar now.

   Please reply.

   From Courtney, the postman.

Courtney Lloyd Jones (8)
Abermule Community Primary School, Montgomery

Dear Goldilocks

Dear Goldilocks,

   I am writing this letter because you came into my house and ate my porridge, broke my chair and slept in my bed and it is not very nice. You probably wouldn't like it if I ate your porridge, broke your chair and slept in your stupid bed that is made out of sand.

   My mum was upset because you broke my favourite chair that I had when I was born and you made a big mess on my bed.

   Plus you ate my favourite porridge that my mum made from our family tradition and we can't make anymore because they don't do the ingredients anymore!

   If you would like to ring us, just type in 698123 and we will tell your mum because you won't tell her yourself, you're too shy.

   Yours sincerely,
   Baby Bear.

Stacey Breese (11)
Abermule Community Primary School, Montgomery

Rapunzel

Once upon a time there was a castle in the woods. In that castle there was a girl called Rapunzel who'd been captured by an evil witch who had locked Rapunzel up in a tower and left her with really long hair.

After three years a man came walking by with a ladder. The man noticed her and leant the ladder against the wall and told Rapunzel to climb down. She did and the man called Tom took her home and married her, and they lived happily ever after.

Natasha Davies (8)
Abermule Community Primary School, Montgomery

Little Red Riding Hood

Once upon a time Little Red Riding Hood was told to go into the scary wood to give some food to her grandmother. When she was walking in the scary wood she had no idea that something was following her. Something jumped out of the bushes, it was a talking lion!

'Argh!'

'Don't be afraid, I just want to know what you are doing in my wood.'

'I am trying to find my grandmother's house.'

'I know where she is.'

'Do you?'

'Yes, I could take you there if you want.'

'But I could drop my food.'

'Can I have some?

'No.'

'Well, I will get her.'

'I can see Grandmother's house, I can give her food.'

But the lion got into Grandma's house and got in bed. Little Red Riding Hood went in and said, 'What big eyes you have and what big teeth you have. Wait ... you are the lion!'

'Yes, and I am going to eat you up.'

Kieran Bebb (8)
Abermule Community Primary School, Montgomery

Letter To The Giant

Dear Mr Giant,

I am writing this letter to inform you that you are no longer welcome to stomp about down here on Earth. My family and I are very angry at the state of our house after you chased poor little Jack from the cottage down the road just to get back your precious golden goose. While you were stomping up on the clouds, the dust from the sky was falling all over the neighbourhood.

Our house is absolutely filthy now and we will have to get a new roof put on which will cost a *lot* of money. Now, as we come home from work or school, builders banging and hammering disturb us and it is most uncomfortable. To summarise, please do not stomp up on the clouds as it causes too much damage down on Earth.

Yours sincerely,

Lucy Wain.

Lucy Wain (11)
Abermule Community Primary School, Montgomery

Little Red Riding Hood

It all started when Little Red Riding Hood asked her mum if she could go and see her dad at work.

Mum replied, 'OK, but be careful through the deep dark forest.'

'Why Mum?'

'Because there are wolves.'

So Little Red Riding Hood set off nervously through the deepest, darkest forest. As she was going along a wolf was watching her. The big mean wolf jumped out of nowhere and said kindly, 'How do you do?'

Little Red Riding Hood just left a big path of dust up in the air, right in front of the wolf's nose.

Aacchhoo!

The wolf was after her and by the time he got over the hill, Red Riding Hood was ready with twenty men and her dad with shotguns. The wolf said considerately, 'I was just going to visit my nan.'

Little Red Riding Hood said, 'I will go with you.'

'No,' said the wolf and ran away fast through the deep dark forest. Little Red Riding Hood followed him sneakily, without him knowing.

As for Red Riding Hood's dad and the gang, well, they were now lost in the deepest, darkest forest.

Rhys Lloyd Evans (9)
Abermule Community Primary School, Montgomery

Rabbit Jack And The Beanstalk

One nice day I, Jack the rabbit, was planting some plants. When I had finished I went to get a glass of cola. When I came back I saw the bean plant as a giant bean plant. It went down to the Earth. I almost forgot, I live in the sky so that's how it's gone down to Earth. I started to climb down the stalk.

When I reached the bottom I saw a giant's home. I went to go inside the giant's house. When I went in the house, I heard a squeaky voice saying, 'Tom, tea's ready.'

When I saw Tom the giant, he was huge; the chair was two-thousand feet.

Tom the giant said, 'I smell the blood of an Englishman.'

I tried to sneak out of the house. I got out of the house and climbed up the beanstalk. When I went up, I bit the stalk so the giant could not climb up the beanstalk.

Conor Jones (8) & Ben Hamer (9)
Abermule Community Primary School, Montgomery

The Three Big Jelly Babies

Once upon a time there were three big jelly babies exploring a village called Abermule. But the jelly babies found it very hard to explore because they couldn't walk, they could only wobble.

One of the jelly babies decided to have a competition to see who could stand up for the longest time. One of them was concentrating so much on the competition; he accidentally stepped on somebody's house. In a few seconds an angry wolf came out of the squashed house. The wolf was absolutely furious. When he came out, he couldn't believe his eyes. The wolf fainted for five seconds!

When the wolf finally woke up, one of the jelly babies had a brilliant idea, it was to use the wolf as a foot pick and so they all used him as a foot pick.

After the three big jelly babies had got all of the pieces of wood and chippings out of their feet they went back to planet jelly babies in their Haribo Star Mix spaceship and the three big jelly babies lived happily ever after.

Josh Jones & Arron Thomas (9)
Abermule Community Primary School, Montgomery

Rapunzel's Gone Bald

One day Rapunzel was singing to herself at the top of the tower. Suddenly, she heard a horse galloping up the road. She looked out of the window and saw a prince coming to rescue her. He asked her to hang her hair down and she did. The prince started to climb up her hair. When he was climbing up her hair, he suddenly felt the hair ripping and dropped with a thump!

The next day when Rapunzel looked in the mirror, she noticed she had no hair! Later the prince woke up and started to climb up the wall and rescued her. On June 22nd they got married and the prince didn't mind that Rapunzel was bald.

Ffion Powell (8) & Sally
Abermule Community Primary School, Montgomery

Hero Billy Hassles Hippo!

Yesterday a hippopotamus escaped from Glasgow Zoo only to be caught by a young schoolboy!

Young Billy Devine found himself alone and facing a large, blue hippo yesterday in the school playground. Unknown to the pupils of Auchinloch Primary School, an escaped hippo had found itself wandering about the area. When Billy saw the newspaper crews and hovering helicopter, he realised that his day was going to be unusual.

Without warning, the hippo charged at Billy but Billy, being so fit dodged it. But the hippo squashed his bag which made him angry so he took off his new shoes and threw them at the hippo! Before he knew it, the hippo turned around and they were face to face and eye to eye. Billy's eyes were full of rage and so were the hippos. The hippo was tense. It charged at Billy but Billy dodged again. He picked up a stick and waited for the hippo to charge again. He threw a stone and it hit the hippo on the foot which made it turn round and charge. Billy dodged and hit the hippo on the back leg and it fell to the ground. He sat on the hippo's leg so it couldn't stand up.

The head teacher, Mrs Lang phoned Glasgow Zoo. Mrs Lang gave the children the rest of the day off and Billy became the school hero.

Reported by Villy Bendie

Billy Devine (12)
Auchinloch Primary School, Glasgow

Robyn Captures Cheetah

Schoolgirl, Robyn Logue aged ten bravely challenged an escaped cheetah to save her school!

Yesterday a cheetah escaped from the local zoo and found its way to Auchinloch Primary School.

'I didn't know what to do because the cheetah was right in front of me. It had piercing eyes and it was crouching down ready to pounce on me,' said Robyn.

She managed to dodge out of its way and grab a rope which was lying on the ground. Climbing up a nearby tree, she tied the rope so that it formed the shape of a hoop. She jumped down and saw the cheetah running towards her. She hid behind the tree and then as fast as she could, threw the rope over the cheetah as she went, but it was too fast. Then she had an idea! She had some food in her bag which she set as a trap. The cheetah ran through the hoop to get the food. As quick as a flash, she pulled on the rope and the cheetah was caught!

The zookeeper's lowered their helicopter and took the startled cheetah back to the zoo. The zoo manager gave Robyn a family pass for the zoo as a reward.

Robyn Logue (11)
Auchinloch Primary School, Glasgow

Scott Tangoes With A Monkey

Yesterday in Auchinloch School playground, young Scott Grant bravely tangled with and captured a fierce monkey when it had escaped from Glasgow Zoo.

Hovering overhead was a helicopter watching closely. Everyone scattered and Scott just stood there in fear or was it with intention!

As this dark brown pale-faced monkey with piercing eyes stared him in the face, Scott could hear the whispering of the people who had sensibly dived for cover. Overhead the helicopter pilot and passengers waited with baited breath. Local newspaper reporters were watching, hoping for the scoop that would give their careers a boost.

Scott attempted to stare the money out but when that didn't work; he went into his bag and got out his lunch to tempt the monkey. It worked! The monkey was caught and taken back to the zoo.

Scott Grant (11)
Auchinloch Primary School, Glasgow

Boy Captures Alligator

Yesterday a vicious man-eating alligator escaped the Glasgow Zoo and was captured by a brave, young schoolboy.

When Amar Aggarwal of Auchinloch Primary arrived at school he came face to face with the vicous reptile. He tried to run away from the creature but wherever he went the alligator followed angrily after him. He ran as fast as he could up the climbing frame but the reptile managed to use its sharp claws to climb up.

Amar said later that he had an idea. He got off the climbing frame as fast as he could. He sprinted down to the bottom of the school where he found some ropes. He quickly tied the ropes around its feet and started to drag the alligator to the monkey bars. 'I tied the other end of the ropes to the bars,' said brave Amar.

He also managed to tie its jaws together but the tail was hard. It was thrashing about and when its tail bashed the wood there was a big bang. Finally, he got the tail tied up.

During his interview, Amar was asked what he felt when the alligator was coming towards him. This is what he said, 'I felt scared and frightened. I didn't know what to do but I found the strength to run. I got the idea to halt it when I saw the ropes and monkey bars and that's how I stopped the alligator'.

Amar Aggarwal (11)
Auchinloch Primary School, Glasgow

The Ali-Gator

Yesterday at 12.30pm Ail Salmi caught an alligator. The items he used were basketballs, nets and a rope.

The alligator escaped from Glasgow Zoo. The boy was not aware at first that the animal was strolling around the playground. He looked down and saw the animal sprinting towards him. He ran up the climbing frame. Fortunately, the alligator could not climb.

The alligator was very fierce. It had green eyes, a very long, slimy tail and a face like a snake. Ail looked all round the playground to find something with which to capture the animal. There were only basketball nets ropes. Now he had a plan. He ran down and grabbed the items. Trying the basketball nets together, he extended the rope to the net. Then he ran around the corner and threw a rock at the alligator.

The animal moved itself towards Ail who let go of the rope, it fell on the animal.

Quickly, the zookeepers rushed in and secured the beast. Mrs Lang, the head teacher said that Ail had been very brave and maybe a little foolish but at least the problem was over.

Aureza Salimy (11)
Auchinloch Primary School, Glasgow

Jo Captures Kangaroo

Schoolboy, Joe Woods, aged ten, captured a kangaroo with only his fists and a net.

Yesterday young Joe astounded the public with his amazing display of bravery and courage. He took on a kangaroo which had escaped from Glasgow Zoo. The animal made its way across Glasgow to Auchinloch Primary School. It was roaming the playground when all the children were in their classrooms. News reporters were en mass. The zookeepers were too scared to contain the animal. However, young Joe arrived late at school because he had been at the dentist. He asked what was going on and one of the zookeepers said that a kangaroo had escaped from the zoo.

'We can't catch it,' he added.

Joe walked slowly towards the animal. Suddenly, a helicopter siren went off and scared the animal away. It ran about the playground. Joe grabbed the zookeeper's net and stick and started to look for the animal. When he saw it, it had its back to him, he took a swipe and hit its back, it ran away.

He didn't give up looking for him. Joe heard a noise and turned around swiftly but not swiftly enough because the kangaroo kicked him. Joe got back up and stunned the kangaroo with the bottom of the stick. Struggling under the weight of the kangaroo, Joe staggered to the zookeepers and gave them the animals.

All of the journalists ran to Joe for an interview. He said, 'I am only too glad to have been able to save the animal.'

The Prime Minister phoned the school and awarded Joe with a holiday to Estapona in Spain. He took the holiday and nothing weird happened in the school again.

Joe Woods (10)
Auchinloch Primary School, Glasgow

Biking

Zooming along the pavement riding really fast, speeding round in circles, crossing the road to school.

Speeding along round the front, riding one-handed at the back. Jumping over crates, pedalling really fast along the road, going home. Now I'm in for tea.

Lyla Murray (10)
Brora Primary School, Brora

Ice Cap

Out on the snowy mountain I stood, shivering and shaking in the freezing coldness. Whispering, harsh winds blew across the crevasse-struck ice cap peaks of the Himalayas and I found myself in a terrible blizzard which made me feel like a prisoner in a cell.

Survival itself was a terrible risk. After a while I began to think of resting but no, I did not stop, I went on, staggering and groaning at the gruelling journey. Now the blizzard was more furious than ever and the colossal balls of snow were falling as if fired from a cannon.

Soon I came to an incredibly steep and slippery part in which dangers were very possible because of the ice, the jagged rocks and the poor visibility. I feared this more than ever, for I had never encountered such a treacherous and dangerous slope before, but I had to be brave.

I quickly gathered up my strength and started on the first rock. I hadn't climbed far when I slipped on one of the rocks and was hurled backwards. I grabbed the sticking out rock from which I had fallen and tried climbing back up but it was no use. I shut my eyes tightly and let go! I fell backwards into a massive, white whirlpool and then into a huge pit of blackness. I went further, further, deeper and deeper …

Puff! I hit my soft pillow and my eyes snapped open. I found myself in my own bedroom, in my own bed with my cover pulled over me. 'Phew!' I said. 'It was all a dream.'

Thomas Bartos (10)
Buckstone Primary School, Edinburgh

My Special Days

On Saturday, 3rd June, my dad went to a rally in Llanybydder. He was rallying his new Honda Civic type-R, he came in first place. His top speed was 140mph, the officials could prove it.

My dad and I were thrilled that he had the trophy in his hands; luckily, we had a trailer because the car would not start and I was so hungry we had to stop in a shop to get something to eat. That was one of the favourite days of my life.

I had another best day. On Sunday, 4th June there was a football tournament in Bow Street. Lots of teams entered, Newcastle Emlyn won in the final against us. We took the lead after my goal but Newcastle Emlyn struck back with a marvellous goal. We were tough enough to score but Darren hit the post. Newcastle Emlyn won the game with another extraordinary goal in the last minute. Those two days were my best days so far this year in 2006.

Dafydd Evans (8)
Cross Inn Primary School, Aberystwyth

On The Battlefield

'Man down, man down!' shouted our sergeant as we got ambushed by the German resistance. In 1995 on October 2nd, we radioed back to base for back-up and artillery from squad X.

We had held them off but we had lost half our squad. We are squad V, we are here to invade Germany. Squad X finally arrived and we overran the German ambush. The artillery was brought up the rear with squad Z.

As we made our way to the first military base in Germany our sergeant divided us into pairs. As we got our heads through the bushes, my partner spotted a jeep leaving the base. We radioed to our sergeant that it was coming our way and that we were to take it out.

When the jeep came through the bushes, squad X strangled the driver and shot the man on the 30 cal on the back. This gave us a good advantage on the Germans. We stripped the Germans and put on their clothes. The 30 cal was full of ammunition and we proceeded into enemy territory. We were nearly into the base when they found out that we were English. They took out one of the snipers from under the sheet on the back of the jeep. We had four other snipers back in the bushes; we had got through the gates so we jumped out and signalled to the sniper to take out their general. Once he was down, the artillery began and we opened fire on them. After say twenty minutes or so, the Germans surrendered. My sergeant went up to the dead general and took his sword.

The artillery had got there and squad Z saw our back-up coming, but squad X saw more Germans. Our back-up had got through the gates when the Germans began to charge. But we still had the sniper in the bushes and we had the jeep. The snipers began and so did the artillery. However, they had so many more men, they also had a tank so we had no chance. We locked our general in a cellar, the tank killed all of our snipers in one shot, we were surrounded. We were taken to another German base and faced a life of torture.

Michael Kirkby-Kent (11)
Cross Inn Primary School, Aberystwyth

When Death Hits You In The Face

Lucy and Gareth ran through the thundering rain and slammed shut the old, white, rotten door to the lighthouse. They stood there, panting and sweating. Gareth wiped his brow with his sleeve. Lucy leant against the door and said, 'Do you think he's gone?'

'I … I don't know, Lucy,' he spluttered.

Suddenly the door rumbled and the wind whistled. 'Something tells me Falco's still there,' Lucy panicked, throwing herself onto the groaning door.

The brass handle turned slowly. Gareth quickly joined Lucy in an attempt to hold the *thing* back. The door could hold on no longer. It smashed to pieces. Lucy's heart stopped dead. Fear was pulsing through her body, she heard penetrating screams rushing through her mind.

Gareth was scared but he held onto his conscience. His wide sapphire eyes saw death but his mind saw determination and the will to keep going.

Falco's dark eyes sought Lucy's. There was a dull sense in the air. His dark ragged jacket flapped in the wind. His huge heavy boots gave a clink as he stepped forward.

'What do you want?' Gareth said bravely.

Falco stared, his sleek, black hair flapped across his angry face. 'It's a full moon tonight, I feel a great hunger.' Huge canine teeth showed.

Lucy pulled back the curtain and a stream of light spilled over Falco's face. He screeched as his eyes burned …

Laura Riddoch (12)
Cultercullen Primary School, Ellon

A Funny Experience

'What do you call the boss of the hankies?'

    'Joanne said a handkerchief.'

    'Not funny.'

    The bell rang and they went in.

    'Come on laugh, grin, at least smile.'

    'Okay, why couldn't the bicycle stand up? It was too tyred!'

    'Ha, that was funny!'

    'Quiet,' the teacher shouted.

Phoebe Corser (12)
Cultercullen Primary School, Ellon

Where Am I?

Am I in space? There's some spaceships, the beams of light. We're in a spaceship, it's red, the same colour as our car.

Wait a minute, there's my sister. This is our car. There's Mum and Dad. It's dark, I'm scared …

Argh!

Lliam Williams (10)
Cultercullen Primary School, Ellon

Sheep

Bo Peep was watching her sheep when all of a sudden she fell asleep and off went one sheep and another and another …

'Let's play hide-and-seek.'

'OK.'

So all three sheep played hide-and-seek.

'I won.'

'Did not.'

'Did so.'

'Let's go to the pen.'

'OK.'

Katie Heslop (11)
Cultercullen Primary School, Ellon

Magic Coin

One day a girl found a magic coin. It was gold with silver in the middle and a big number on the silver bit.

The girl took the coin to school to show her friends, they liked it. She showed her mum, she said it was a two pound coin.

Lauren Tilley (8)
Glyncoed Junior School, Cardiff

Snow White Turns Into A Monster

One rainy night Snow White was getting ready to go to the mall with the prince. Then two hours later, the doorbell rang and it was the prince. The prince said, 'Shall we go to the mall now?'

'Yes,' said Snow White. Then five minutes later they arrived at the mall.

'Let us dance,' said the prince.

'OK,' said Snow White and so they started dancing.

At two in the morning the prince said, 'I need to get home because I am getting really tired.'

The prince said bye to Snow White then Snow White got mad because she wanted to dance some more. She turned into a monster and followed him to see if the prince was going to bed. He was not going to bed so Snow White tried to kill the prince with her claws and her sharp teeth. The prince got out his sword and tried to kill Snow White. The prince said, 'I love you,' and the monster turned back into Snow White. They got married and had three babies and lived happily ever after.

Ryan Butler (8)
Glyncoed Junior School, Cardiff

Snow White Turns Into A Bogeyman

Once upon a time there lived a little girl called Snow White. She was kind and generous and lived by herself.

One day she was walking to the Pizza Palace because that is where she worked. This old lady stopped her and said to Snow White, 'Do you want an apple my love?'

'No thank you,' said Snow White, 'I have to get to the Pizza Palace because I'm late for work.'

The old lady said that she would drop Snow White off at work in her helicopter.

Snow White said, 'OK then, thank you, you're very kind.'

When they were flying, the lady finally gave Snow White an apple. Suddenly, Snow White turned into a bogeyman! She blew up the helicopter and landed on everyone. Some people survived and some people died.

Snow White stomped over to the Pizza Palace to go and do her job. When she got there her boss Martin screamed the palace down.

The next day Snow White woke up and found herself in a tiny bed. All little men were around her, she asked them what their names were. They said their names were Dopey, Spotty, Sleepy, Lazy and Bumpty.

'Hello,' said Snow White.

'Hello,' said the dwarves. 'We are going to work.' Then they picked up spades and shovels and left. On the way they sang a song, it goes like this. 'Hi ho, hi ho, it's off to work we go with a shovel and spade and a walking stick, hi ho, hi ho.'

Snow White was clapping but then she fainted.

A handsome prince picked up Snow White and kissed her on the lips and then the spell was broken, the spell that had made Snow White into a bogeyman!

Harry Morgan (8)
Glyncoed Junior School, Cardiff

Louie And The Beanstalk

Once there lived a little boy called Louie and his mother, Alicia. Alicia was a widow. She and her son Louie were very poor. They needed lots of money. They had five pigs so they decided to sell them but nobody wanted them.

Next day, Louie found a lottery ticket in the dustbin. In the night, Alicia listened to the radio and all the lottery numbers she had were called out.

'Yes!' said Alicia. 'I have won five million pounds.'

'What!' said Louie. 'We have won the lottery!'

'Yeah!'

In four weeks they were poor again and they decided to sell their cow called Daisy. A man gave Louie magic pennies to plant. Louie went home and planted the pennies. Two days later the pennies turned into a bronze beanstalk. Louie climbed up it and there he found two original-sized doors. He opened them; there he saw a terrifying monster. Luckily he was camouflaged.

Louie spotted a goose, the goose was laying fifty pound notes. 'I'm going to steal that goose,' said Louie. And so he did. He took it home and cut down the beanstalk and there everybody lived happily ever after.

Natasja Paris (8)
Glyncoed Junior School, Cardiff

Jack And The Beanstalk

One day Jack and his friends went on the bus. They got off the bus, Jack saw the beanstalk. Jack tried to climb up it. Then Jack saw the giant. Jack ran into the giant's castle.

They saw the giant. Jack ran into a big bag, the giant smiled. Jack was scared. The giant thought to himself, *I'm going to have my tea now.*

Jack snuck out of the castle. Jack saw his mum, they hugged.

Ellie Atkins-Tate (8)
Glyncoed Junior School, Cardiff

Snow White

Dear Snow White,

A wolf broke into our house and took your purse but he left a poisonous apple and he said not to tell you, so don't eat the apple in the house or you will die!

I will see you when you come back from work. Quick, the wolf has come back to the house, hurry up now, he has stolen my hat.

From

One of the Seven Dwarves.

Shanice Lane (8)
Glyncoed Junior School, Cardiff

In A Dragon's Cave

Help! I'm stuck, I'm in a cave. I feel scared, I want to go home. There's a dragon, it's going to eat me, *argh!*

The cave door opens, I run out as fast as I can. I see my mum, I jump into her arms and we walked home.

Emily Huxtable (9)
Glyncoed Junior School, Cardiff

The Empty House

Hi, my name's Samantha (everyone calls me Sam) I am eleven years old. This is what happened two weeks ago.

Yawn! Another day.

'Hi Sam,' called the postman.

'Hi um,' I said. (I didn't know his name.)

'Just call me Jerry.'

Then he disappeared!

When I was cleaning the house there was a knock at the door. When I answered it there was nothing there except an envelope, I opened it and this is what it said: 'Do not go to the empty house! J'. Who on earth was J?

The next day I went exploring the village and went to the empty house. (I forgot about the letter.) I opened the door and bats came flying out, I screamed but still carried on. A dark figure came out beyond the shadows and grabbed me and held me tight. I could not get free even though I kicked him and struggled.

He locked me in some room and the postman was there! I was so pleased, I smiled (even though I wondered what was going on) I asked him, 'What is going on Jerry?'

Jerry replied, 'This man, Jack, is trying to rule this village. I should not be telling you this but the people in this village want you to lead them. Anyway, he wants to kill you.'

Then Jack came and the postman was fighting. After that Jack went to jail and I ruled happily ever after.

Yasmin Ghahremani (10)
Glyncoed Junior School, Cardiff

The Old Man

The old man was sitting on the bench. A boy was walking his dog on the field. He stopped, he looked at the old man and then he walked along.

The old man went home, the boy lived near him, the boy said, 'Hi,' the man went in.

Keeley Fashan (9)
Glyncoed Junior School, Cardiff

The Horrible Spell

Put spaghetti Bolognese in a bowl, stir it round then add slimy guts of snails. Later put some tomato sauce in, add exhaust pipe. Later go and get a dog and stir it round. Afterwards go and get green massive bogeys and then take a fork.

Swallow!

Ghazi Ayoub (10)
Glyncoed Junior School, Cardiff

One Night

One night I was all alone downstairs, my mum was upstairs. I don't know what she was doing so I went to see. I was halfway up the stairs when I heard a voice, it didn't sound like my mum, it was a deep and scary voice. This is where my story begins …

I peeked round the corner, there was nothing there. I went into my mum's room, I heard something, it sounded like someone was whispering in my ear. I shouted as loud as I could.

'Hello, is anyone there?' But there was no reply. I thought I was the only one in the house until I saw a dark shadow coming towards me.

The door slowly shut and it suddenly got very dark. A little light peeked out through the cupboard, I opened it. The next thing I knew, I was on the floor and I couldn't get up. There was something next to me right now, I feel like saying I woke up and it was all a dream, I can't because it wasn't a dream. I turned my head and saw something, it looked familiar and then I realised what it was!

When I was five I had an imaginary friend, I know it's weird but that was the only friend I had, but now I've got plenty, I'd forgotten about my old imaginary friend and now this was getting spooky …

Wanawsha Maroof (10)
Glyncoed Junior School, Cardiff

The Long Journey

Once upon a time there was a spaceship landing on the moon. There were four people on the moon, their names where Bob, Sam, Jack and Sue. They were the first people on the moon. They were there to explore the moon, they found a moon monster so they tried to use their space guns but they didn't work and so they ran. Sue screamed and sixty-two moon monsters came. They ran to the spaceship, they tried to start it but it wouldn't start. Bob jumped out and ran away. No one went after him.

Bob came to the moon monster's main base to start the ship. They needed a stone from the moon monster's base.

Sue said to Sam and Jack that she could see what the moon monsters were up to. Sue set off and she found their moon monster base and ran to get the stone. Sadly she got shot by a moon monster. It was up to Sam and Jack; they found out that the moon monsters were going to attack the Earth!

It was up to Sam and Jack to save Earth. Sam and Jack made their own gun which would kill the moon monster and so they went to attack. There was a moon monster which had the stone and lots of others watching it, they thought of a plan. Then Sam said he would get the ship ready, Jack went to attack the main base. Jack got the stone and ran as fast as he could.

Sam Norman (10)
Glyncoed Junior School, Cardiff

The Potion

In my potion I will have … slugs slime, frogs' legs, fish eyes, a dog's tail, someone's heart, mashed up flies, cats' ears, ants' heads and lots more! I was going to give it to someone in my class called Kelly, I hate her. She was the one who took all my friends off me. I hoped this potion would work.

All of a sudden I heard footsteps coming up the stairs, oh no, it was my mum, I had to hide the potion somewhere, but where? I know, under the towel. Luckily, she only went into her room to get something. *That was lucky,* I thought to myself. I put foil over the potion and hid it in my cupboard.

The next morning I took the foil off the tub of potion and poured it into a drink bottle. When I got to school, I was so excited to give Kelly the potion! It was going to be funny.

Yeah, it was finally home time, I got the bottle out of my bag and Kelly asked me, what it was. I said, 'A new fizzy bottle of pop.'

She replied, 'Could I have some?'

I said, 'Of course, here we go.'

Suddenly, she took a big sip and started acting like she was drunk. But then she started being nice, it was so weird.

The next day she was acting like she was my best friend but at least I got my friends back. When I got home, I was so glad the potion had worked, I was so happy, oh yes!

Lauren Smith (9)
Glyncoed Junior School, Cardiff

The Man-Eating Sea Monster

One day a boy called Bond who had big, scary, creepy eyes was at the seaside with his big monster hair planning to trick others. Bond was going fast, speeding like a gold shedding arrow.

Everyone kept getting in his way; he wanted to go faster than everyone so he thought of a plan. He was going to dress like a sea monster to scare everyone in the sea.

George screamed saying, 'Help me, there's a sea monster after me, run, sea monster!'

George went running out of the sea.

'Help me, there's a sea monster after me!' Bond scared everyone away.

The sunset was just on its way down. Bond had the seaside to himself for one week. During the week he met a real sea monster with sharp teeth and a long, black, spiky tail. Bond went running out of the sea. Bond wished he hadn't played his tricks, as what goes around comes around! Bond had to sit outside all summer and watch others in the sea.

Michael Jones (9)
Guilsfield CP School, Welshpool

The Big Monster Rabbit

One summer day at around lunchtime, Kieran was in his field picking corn when he noticed much of his corn had been nibbled away. He was getting fed up of this and needed a plan.

Kieran had floppy ears like a rabbit, all he needed was a white fluffy tail and he would be the scariest rabbit on the field.

The next day they were there, Kieran got in his rabbit costume and scared them away by running at them. They ran into the woods and down the lane, they didn't come back for a week.

Kieran was relieved that they didn't come back for a week, he laughed to himself as he couldn't believe that they thought they had seen a giant monster rabbit.

In one week they came back and started to ruin all the crops again, Kieran immediately put on his costume and frightened them away again. He felt happy with himself but he was in for a surprise of his own. He came face to face with a bigger and scarier girl rabbit.

Ryan Phillips (9)
Guilsfield CP School, Welshpool

The Man-Biting Guard Dog

One beautiful summer morning, I went to watch the racing cars in the racing ground with my dad. There were two days of racing, on Saturday and Sunday.

Everyone was really bugging me, every time I moved my head, they moved their heads as well because they kept looking back at me. When the race was finished, I slammed the house door right open and I shouted, 'Mum, Mum.'

'What Cameron?' said my mum.

'I did not like racing today, it was awful! There was a teenager in front of me and he kept looking back at me every time.'

'But Cameron you're fourteen years old.'

'Mum, I'm short.'

'I know that,' said Mum.

I came up with an idea that day. I live nearby. Dad did not come with me to the racing this time, I dressed up as a guard dog.

It was horrific, that boy was in front of me, he looked back again and I went to him, 'Woof!' He went down the steps to tell his manager. I said in my head, *he's a grass.*

The manager was tall, thin and he looked like a fast runner, he came stomping up the steps. I said, 'Oh no.' I thought for a second I was thinking, *I know what to do, I'll growl at him and scare everyone off that annoys me!*

'Bark, bark, roar!'

I had the whole stadium to myself, it was fabulous and I could run around and get fit by running around the stadium. There was a f-f-f-fierce dog there and I said, 'Oh no!' She came growling over to me as fast as she could. I jumped out of my suit quickly!

A week later I went by myself and stayed on the stadium and just watched as I normally would because I didn't want to see that dog again.

Cameron Davies (9)
Guilsfield CP School, Welshpool

The Crocodile's Lake

Once there was a little girl named Eleanor, she lived in sunny Spain. The sun was beaming down on everyone. In the part of Spain where Eleanor lived it was especially hot. Eleanor had a pointy nose like a crocodile and big, beady, yellow eyes. She also had pointy sharp teeth.

Eleanor was a great swimmer. It was so hot Eleanor went for a swim in the nearby lake but it was too crowded to swim and she bashed into Alan. This was no good so she had a plan. She went home and dressed up, she was a crocodile. She went back to the lake and shouted, 'Crocodile!' Everybody rushed away.

For a week no one dared go back, everyone was telling Eleanor to get out of that lake. 'Get out!' they shouted over and over again.

'No,' she said, 'there's no crocodile in this lake.'

'Yes, there is!' they said.

Helen said, 'I am tired of seeing her swimming back and forth.'

For three days she had the lake all to herself but when the lake was full with people again and she started swimming back and forth, she bashed into the Thomas family and so again, she got out and dressed up.

This time Eleanor crashed into a member of the Thomas family, he screamed, 'Help! Crocodile!' Everybody rushed away in horror but this time for a week. Eleanor was back and forth again enjoying the space to herself.

All the other families were getting bored of seeing Eleanor swimming back and forth. But this time it was Alan who said, 'Let's go back into the lake.'

Eleanor ran home and used her plan again but when she got to the lake her plan backfired on her. There was a *real crocodile* asking if she wanted to go catch some fish with him. She zoomed away, like a golden arrow and never came back!

Eleanor Thomas (9)
Guilsfield CP School, Welshpool

The Rampage

One hot and sunny day at Menivill Hills, Bonny was running so quick you couldn't see him. One day they built a skatepark there. 'This isn't fair, I loved running around here,' said Bonny. I've got an idea; I will dress up as a cheetah and frighten people away.

Bonny in his disguise approached the skaters slyly. A small child caught sight of Bonny but did not realise that he was a boy.

'Quick, run, cheetah on the loose!'

For the next three days no one went to the skateboard park. He ran up and down the half-pipe like lightning. Enjoying having the park all to himself. After a few days the people got fed up of watching Bonny having fun and so they all came back.

The people were getting in his way again so he put on his cheetah suit and scared them away.

Joey didn't know that when you come face to face with a cheetah the thing to do is stand still.

'Quick, run, cheetah on the loose!' said Joey.

'Argh,' screamed all the other people.

The next day Joey was really brave. He got out his skateboard and started skating again. All the people came back. Bonny was getting ready, he had his T-shirt on, he was in the tree and he heard a noise. *'Argh,* a real cheetah!' he shouted.

He jumped out of the tree and ran as fast as he could, back to the safety of his home. All the people saw him running back towards his house.

Later on in the week he would not go running again. All the other children would be playing happily but not Bonny, his plan had backfired.

Andrew Davies (9)
Guilsfield CP School, Welshpool

The Pearl Family

One freezing Wednesday morning in the forest, the skiers came to ski in Oliver's favourite playing place. Every time he tried to play, skiers got in his way. He moved around the slopes like a silver arrow but because the place was so busy he kept bumping into Charlotte, Garion or Mollie. Oliver was becoming frustrated so he decided to put on his wolf costume and scare the skiers away.

'Argh! There's a wolf, run, wolf!' Oliver had eyes like a wolf and teeth like a wolf. What Charlotte didn't know was that when you come face to face with a roaring wolf you should just pretend to put some more clothes on and ignore it.

No one dared to go after the wolf so Oliver had the forest to himself for a whole day. His friends said to him, 'Get out of there, there's a wolf in the wood.'

'A wolf, don't be stupid.' Oliver knew differently.

Some brave people started skiing again, they were really having fun but then Oliver scared everybody away.

'Argh, there's a wolf, wolf, run!' Garion was learning how to swerve in and out of trees at the time. What Garion didn't know was that if you come face to face with a wolf you should just walk away and pretend to put some warmer clothes on.

No one dared go there three days after this last fright. Oliver was enjoying himself so much gliding down the crystal-white snow until people started coming back. But this time Oliver heard a funny noise and he went to see what it was. It was ... 'Oh, it's only a cat,' he sighed with relief and he went back to the slopes.

Charlotte was learning how to stand on her head. In a second she was face to face with a wolf, 'Argh!'

What Charlotte didn't know was that when you come face to face with a wolf you should just pretend that you were just going to put some warmer clothes on and walk away.

She screamed and shouted, 'Wolf, run, wolf!' There were people picking up kids and people picking up dogs and in a second everybody was gone.

Oliver had the forest to himself for a week. Many people were telling Oliver to get off the slopes that they had a wolf on the prowl but he didn't listen. He should have though!

After a week some brave people started coming back onto the slopes. Oliver was about to get changed again into his costume when he heard a funny noise. He went to see what it was. He thought it was a cat again but it wasn't, it was a wolf.

'*Argh!*' he screamed and Garion came to see what the matter was.

Garion screamed, 'Oh my God.' Garion told everybody that the scary wolf originally had been Oliver but he had been paid back for tricking them all. Oliver ran all the way home and barricaded his door for a week as he was terrified of the wolf and felt very embarrassed.

Kate Williams (9)
Guilsfield CP School, Welshpool

An Unlikely Surprise!

Many years ago there was an iguanodon called Charlie, he looked a lot like a T-rex. He had sharp pointed teeth and huge feet and was bored, every day the same thing happened.

One day he went to the great plain to doze. When he awoke it was night, almost immediately he thought of a game. He ran over the grass and then jumped into the pond, then it got dark and he went to sleep. The next day he tried to play his game but people got in his way. *Bang!* he bumped into Mrs Crunch. *Splash!* he landed on Mrs Aput.

Charlie was getting very annoyed and then he came up with a plan.

The next day he stayed in the forest. When his mum and dad had gone, he started rolling in a mud puddle. When he had finished he was all brown, when the mud had dried he looked like a T-rex. He tried his roar, it sounded good, then he decided to scare everybody out of the pond.

Mr and Mrs Joe were having a bath close to the shore, Charlie went up slowly to them. Mrs Joe turned and saw Charlie, 'T-rex, T-rex,' shouted Mrs Joe. After everyone heard her they ran to the other side of the river.

For the next three days Charlie had the plain to himself whilst the others watched helplessly from the side. The others got annoyed and in no time the plain was full of happy people. Charlie went into the forest and got in the mud. He decided to scare Mr Terasaw, playing close to the forest. He sneaked up and gave a loud roar.

'T-rex, T-rex,' shouted Mrs Terasaw.

In no time at all everybody was on the other side of the river. Charlie had it for a whole week but of course the others came back after that. Charlie went into the forest for a third time but before he got out, he bumped into something big, brown and scary.

'T-rex, T-rex!' screamed Charlie.

He ran out of the forest still looking like a T-rex. He jumped into the river and swam. When he got to the other side all the mud had fallen off and everyone could see what he had done. For the rest of the summer Charlie stayed on that side of the river thinking, *what goes around comes around!*

Oliver Hart (9)
Guilsfield CP School, Welshpool

Jasper And The Tiger

One day Jasper was looking after the animals in the forest when the Jones family came and started throwing stones and sticks at the tigers. Jasper was not very impressed by them so he disguised himself as a tiger. He then went and hid in the grass and waited until they went by. As they went by he scared the Jones family with a loud roar.

The thing to do when faced with a tiger, is to stay still and let it go past, but the Jones family didn't know this. The Jones family screamed as loud as they could, 'Tiger! Tiger! Run away!' No one went in the forest for three days.

The next family to enter the forest were the Williams family. As soon as they had got there, they started to throw stones and sticks at the animals. So Jasper dressed up as a tiger again and hid in the grass until they went past. When they went past they scared them with a *roar!* The thing to do when you are faced with a tiger is stay still and let it pass but the Williams family didn't know this, 'Tiger! Tiger! Run away!' No one went in the forest for one week.

After one week the Williams family children started to come back. As soon as they were there they started to throw stones and sticks again at the tigers. Jasper couldn't believe it. How dare people treat wild animals like this and so Jasper dressed up like a tiger again and scared the family away. This final time he hoped the families had learnt their lesson as next time it may not be a human dressed as a tiger, the next time it may be a real tiger and he would not be so kind!

George Dyer (8)
Guilsfield CP School, Welshpool

Man-Eating Tiger

One day there was a girl called Lizzie. She had blue eyes that looked a bit like tiger's eyes; she had a brother called Michel, a dad called Ben and an uncle called Matt. Matt lived in a jungle full of wildlife. There were bears, tigers, snakes and so many more.

'I think it's time to see your uncle Matt.'

'OK,' Lizzie and Michel said.

'Where does he live?'

'Well, let's say by the jungle.'

'Can we play in the jungle?'

'Oh yes of course, you can Lizzie, any time you want.'

'Are there bears?' said Michel

'I don't know, there may be,' said Ben.

'I hope there is,' said Lizzie.

'When are we going?'

'Well, I will wake you up tonight.'

'OK,' said Michel and Lizzie.

One hour later they all went to bed so excited about the trip to the jungle.

'Lizzie, Michel,' Ben said in a whisper, 'it is time to wake up.'

'It's time already?'

'Yes, now come on, we don't want to be late.'

'Are we there yet?' said Lizzie.

'No, we are not there yet.'

'Are we there yet?' said Lizzie.

'No, we're not there yet.'

'Are we there *yet?*'

'*No, no, no!* We are not there yet!'

'Are we there yet?'

'Yes, we are here,' said Michel.

'At last,' said Lizzie.

'Have you got your bags?' said Ben.

'Yes, we have,' they all said.

'Come on, let's go.'

It took a long time to get to the jungle but they got there in the end.

'Is this his house?'

'Yes,' said Ben, 'it is.'

Ben rang on the doorbell and a very fat man came to the door. 'Hello kids, I want a word with your dad, go and play in the jungle for a few minutes.'

'OK,' Lizzie and Michel said and off they went.

'There are too many people, I can't see any wildlife,' said Lizzie.
'Let's go.'

The next day Lizzie was fed up with all of the people in the jungle so she dressed up as a tiger. Her eyes glowed in the sunlight which made them look like a tiger even more. She crawled out of the house and into the jungle. She sneaked up on the baker. The thing to do when you see a tiger is sneak out very quietly, he did not.

'Help, help! there's a tiger!'

All of the people in the jungle ran as fast as they could out of the jungle.

'At last,' said Lizzie, 'there's no more people in the jungle, I have it all to myself.'

Lizzie had the jungle to herself for four days; no one dared share the jungle with a man-eating tiger! Lizzie took off her costume and ran all around the jungle looking for wildlife.

'Come inside at once, there is a tiger out there!' shouted Uncle Matt.

'I am sure it has gone,' said Lizzie and ran deeper into the jungle.

The people were getting bored and one brave man ran into the jungle. Everyone followed and at once every one was playing in the jungle. So Lizzie put on her costume and scared the butcher. The thing to do when you see a tiger is to creep out quietly. He did not know this, 'Help, help! There's a tiger!'

The whole jungle ran out, Lizzie had the jungle to herself for another week. Everyone was very bored at home but Lizzie was having the time of her life until she met a cub that said, 'Hello Mummy, I thought you were going shopping?'

'Argh!' she said and ran. The people knew at once and saw what she was doing. Her dad told her off and they all went home, her cruel trick had spoilt the whole family's outing.

Charlotte Peake (9)
Guilsfield CP School, Welshpool

The Huge Alligator

Once upon a time there was a little girl called Lisa, she had alligator talents at swimming and could hold her breath for an exceedingly long time, she also had alligator teeth.

She lived in a lovely valley called Primrose Valley. Lisa was incredibly good at acting but there wasn't any TV scripts including an alligator so she took up fishing instead. She managed to eat eight types of fish in just ten minutes.

One day when Lisa was fishing, people started to go there so there wasn't as many fish for her to catch and so she came up with a plan. Out of plastic she made a mask, the top half of an alligator's head, where the eyes were supposed to be there were holes so she could see out where she was going. When she came to the dam, she went fishing, saying quietly, 'I'm going to scare the lot of them and then I'm going to catch every fish in the dam!'

When she had finished saying this she spotted John and Joe from the Jones family fishing in a rowing boat. Lisa swam up to the boat and slowly lifted up the mask out of the water. The boys didn't know that if you saw a flesh-eating alligator, the thing to do is row your boat back to shore as if you had forgotten a bucket of worms, for when they saw Lisa they shouted together, 'An alligator, alligator in the water!' They rowed their boat back to shore and everyone followed.

When everybody had reached the shore they stared at the top half. 'A huge flesh-eating alligator head,' they shouted. After this incident no one went to the dam for three days, all except Lisa. One day when Lisa was out fishing she caught five fish in ten minutes!

As they approached in almost a blink of an eye, her friends boomed down at her from their little rowing boat, 'Lisa, come out of this dam this instant, there is a flesh-eating alligator in that dam, come out at once!'

'No chance, you're pulling my leg, it is probably a vegetarian alligator, you know.'

Some brave people who were tired of seeing Lisa catching fish in almost a blink of an eye fetched their rowing boats and fishing rods and soon enough Primrose dam was full again of happy fisherman. But Lisa had grown to like having the dam all to herself so she rowed her boat out of sight, put her diving suit on and her alligator mask, and silently swam back to the crowds of fishermen.

Mr Brown, the ice cream man, was humming to himself while he waited to catch some fish. Lisa dived under the water, took hold of the hook and pulled it. She felt the line going up and when the mask showed Mr Brown screamed like the littlest girl ever.

'*Argh!* Alligator in the water,' everyone screamed, and so the dam was empty once again, Lisa had the dam all to herself for one whole week.

Everyone was beginning to feel bored of watching Lisa catching all the fish. They decided they had had enough and soon everyone was fishing again and so Lisa went to put her costume on and when she was swimming back she realised she was not alone! When Lisa turned around there was a boy alligator, he said, 'You are the girl of my dreams, marry me or else I will eat you!'

Lisa swam to the shore shouting, 'Alligator, alligator in the water!' When everyone saw her they knew she had pretended to be the alligator and so after that Lisa never went fishing again.

Amy Barber-Brown (9)
Guilsfield CP School, Welshpool

The Fox And The Picnic

It was a hot sunny day in New York. The sky was a clear sparkling azure. Ryan was having a good time in the city park.

Ryan was playing on the slide. Up the steps and down the slide over and over again. Suddenly, he saw Mr Jones, his teacher, coming with his daughter Emma carrying a picnic. Emma ran to the slide.

'Oh no!' said Ryan. 'I wanted to have the park to myself, I don't want to share it. I must think of a plan to get rid of them.'

The next day bright and early, Ryan was working on the plan. At lunchtime Ryan went back to the City Park, this time he was wearing his disguise. He was the scariest fox you have ever seen.

Mr Jones and Emma were sitting on the grass eating a picnic when the fox came from the bush and stole some of the picnic. Emma screamed and ran away shouting, 'Fox! Fox!'

Mr Jones ran after her. Ryan was happy because his plan had worked.

The next day Ryan was playing on the slide, dressed like a scary fox when Mrs Orr the nurse, and Kieran, her son, came with their picnic. Kieran ran straight to the slide. Ryan ran behind the bush. When they started to eat their picnic, Ryan the fox crept from behind the bush and stole the cake. Mrs Orr jumped up and screamed, 'Fox! Fox!' As she ran away with Kieran running away after her.

Ryan was happy about his plan working, he was having a great day until he was ready to go home. He was hungry and tired but when he got to the gates, he was shocked to see a policeman stopping the people going to the park. There was a big notice saying: *Wild Fox Beware!* And the gates were closed and locked. Ryan went back to the slide, he was feeling very sorry. Ryan lay down and went to sleep.

Ryan was woken up by a girl fox licking his ears. He jumped up and ran away to the park gates shouting, 'Fox! Fox!' Throwing off his costume on the way. The policeman unlocked the gates and let him out. Ryan was happy to be going home and he said to himself, 'I will not be selfish again.'

Ryan Jones (10)
Guilsfield CP School, Welshpool

The Man-Eating Leopard

Once there was a young boy called Garion. He lived near a very tall oak tree. Garion always climbed the tree. His face had freckles like spots of a leopard; his head was like that of a leopard and eyes like a leopard. He was a fantastic runner. He ran across the fields at one hundred miles per hour. Since it was summer more people got in the way and Garion could not run as fast so he made a plan.

He went inside and got his spotty coat, he made a leopard-like tail. He went outside quietly. Bob, the zookeeper, was having a day off. Then Garion (as the leopard) roared at Bob, but Bob didn't know that if you see a leopard staring at you, the thing to do is to walk back quietly.

Bob screamed, 'Leopard, leopard!'

Bob ran so fast that dust was left in the air. Everyone followed him and Garion had the field all to himself once again.

A family called the Browns were having a day off, they had travelled from Germany. They had taken a picnic to share, when the cheerful family where about to have their tuna and mayonnaise sandwiches they were shocked because someone had stolen their food. They saw a leopard eating the chocolate fudge cake with a cherry on top. The Browns opened their mouths as wide as possible, they all screamed, 'Leopard, leopard!' In less than fourteen seconds, they had all run away. Garion had the place to himself again, he ran at one thousand miles per hour.

He was really enjoying the freedom when all of a sudden he did not feel alone anymore. He saw a female leopard right next to him. The female leopard asked Garion if he would marry her. She also told him that they would live in a tall tree. Garion was shocked at the offer by the talking leopard! He couldn't quite believe what he was about to do but he found himself answering the leopard, 'I really like the idea but I'd better not as my family will miss me. Maybe see you later.'

Garion, feeling slightly hot, ran like Sonic. He could not believe what had just happened. He was pleased to get back home safely. Garion never played a trick again, he had learnt his lesson. Garion never ran again in his whole entire life and Garion was so sad he tried to run but his feet would not let him.

Garion Brown (9)
Guilsfield CP School, Welshpool

The Golden Rage

One hot sunny day in Africa, Camilla was standing on a moss-covered tree trunk in amongst boiling orange sand. All she could smell was the fragrance of evergreen trees from Great Green Wood all around her. Now, Camilla was no smarter or bigger than anyone else, but Camilla was the best at imitating animals. Her best was a lion. She sounded just like a real lion; she even looked like a lion too, with lionish hair, teeth and eyes. She loved to practise her lion impressions in Great Green Wood. But one day people started coming and shouting at her to be quiet so she thought of a cunning plan.

She disguised herself as a lion by making a lion costume out of gold fur (fake fur of course) and went into Great Green Wood. She did the loudest roar she could. 'Roooaaarrr!' She looked so much like a lion that everyone screamed. Jenny from the Davidson family shouted, 'Oh no, lion, quick run away, it is going to eat you!'

The thing to do when you come face to face with a lion, you should just walk away slowly. But these people did not know that. They all ran away screaming. Camilla had the forest to herself for three days after that.

After three days was up, people started going back to Great Green Wood. Camilla was, furious she wanted the wood all to herself.

'Right, I am going to dress up again,' mumbled Camilla.

'What was that?' chanted the Davidson family.

'Nothing, I was just saying I can't wait for my fancy dress party.'

'Are you sure?'

'Yes, yes, I'm sure.'

'Okay then, bye.'

When Camilla got home she snatched her lion disguise from under her bed and walked out of the room.

In Great Green Wood everyone was having a great time. Laughing and playing, jumping and dancing. Emily, the mechanic, on the other hand thought she could see the leaves in the bush moving when, 'Roooaaarrr!' Emily was terrified, she screamed, 'Oh no, lion! Quick, run away, it is going to eat you!' Camilla had the wood to herself for seven days.

Seven days were up and brave people started to wander round the forest again. Camilla was angrier than ever.

'I can't stand this, I'll dress up again.'

'What was that love?' said Emily.

'Nothing.'

The next day Camilla went back thinking her usual thoughts, who she was going to scare next. When Camilla got there she screamed, *'Argh!* Lion! Quick, run away, it is going to eat you!'

She was caught out. Everyone had seen what she had done. The only trouble was the lion she had seen was a boy lion and he had fallen in love with her and was following her. Somebody got a net and caught the lion but Camilla was too scared to go there for a month after that.

The moral of the story is what goes around comes around.

Mary-Morgan Griffiths (9)
Guilsfield CP School, Welshpool

Goldilocks And The Three Bears

Once upon a time there was a little girl called Goldilocks. When she was about five years old, she got chucked out of her house because she was too much trouble.

Six years later, she found herself roaming the streets all alone with nobody to keep her company.

One day she found a little cottage just outside of town. She knocked on the door. There was no answer, so she pulled the handle to see if it was open and it was. She stepped inside and had a look in the cupboards for some food because she was famished.

Two or three hours later she was sitting in the living area when she heard the door open.

'We are back at last,' said a tiny voice.

'I'm never doing this again,' someone else said in a deeper voice.

Goldilocks quickly scrambled up the stairs and hid under the bed in one of the bedrooms. A big thump hit the stairs. *Boom! Boom! Boom!* She felt herself trembling, shivering and shaking all at the same time. The big, huge man she thought might be the dad looked under the bed and he saw her ...

Evie Gale (11)
Innerwick Primary School, Dunbar

One Clone, One Battle

Kamino is the home planet of all Clones. I was called Bly. I was ready for combat any time. The mission was to wipe out 20,000,000 battle Droids from Corusant. 10,000,000 of us took off in Republic gunships to the Jedi temple.

We arrived. A Jedi moved into the battle and … *bang!* Mines blew up everyone including the Jedi, except me, Bly. I used all my ammo and there was still loads left. It seemed to be impossible. I kicked and punched them but there were still 10,000,000 left. I noticed that there was a light saber. I picked it up and killed them easily. There was one left and …

A gunship came and landed on it, *crack!* A bunch of Clones and a commander came out. The commander said, 'Where are they?'

'Dead, Sir,' I answered.

'OK, Cmmander.'

'But I'm not a Commander,' I said.

After that I was known as Commander Bly.

Five years later on Mygeeto with Ki-Adi-Mundi, we had to fend off the battle and super battle Droids to wipe out the CIS to protect the Republic. The Jedi didn't know about our plan until I got a call through my COM. Order 66. It was time to kill all Jedi.

I crept up behind Ki-Adi with two Clones. We shot 60 bullets into him. Only three Jedi survived the triadic order 66. Jedi lord Yoda who barely escaped from Kashyyk, Obi-Wan Kenobi who defeated the four armed General Grievous half alien half robot Sep leader and Anakin Skywalker better known as Darth Vader …

Ryan Reid (10)
Innerwick Primary School, Dunbar

Red Riding Hood

Red Riding Hood was a good little girl who lived in the heart of Glasgow. She lived with her mum, dad and her dog, Izy. They were a happy family with lots of money, a big house and, of course, their lovely daughter Little Red Riding Hood. But Red Riding Hood wasn't all good, she was a little bit evil.

One day she went to see her granny with some money. She was walking along when she saw a gang of boys coming towards her. *'Help!'* she said in her mind. She started to run towards them to dodge them, but there were so many of them, she couldn't get past. So she decided she would phone her mum, but her mum's phone was engaged. So she decided to phone her granny.

After a few minutes she saw her granny coming with a saucepan. Red Riding Hood was amazed that her granny had come with a saucepan to shoo them off. When her granny saw Red Riding Hood, she came rushing over to see her.

'Your mum phoned me to say you were coming over to see me with something for me.'

'Yes,' said Red Riding Hood.

Red Riding Hood had always been sick of wearing a red cloak, a red dress and a red ribbon in her hair, so she decided to steal a little bit of the money that she was giving to her granny.

'Yes, my mum gave me some money for you.'

Secretly, she took some money. Once she had given her granny the money, she went down to H&M and bought a blue mini skirt, a purple crop top and a pair of high heels.

Holly Letch (10)
Innerwick Primary School, Dunbar

Little Red Riding Hood

Dear Mr Wolf,

What have you done with my gran? I went in and it was *you* who was in my gran's cottage. I knocked at the door and I went in, but she was not there. So, what have you done with her?

I love my gran so much and I have milk and cookies for her. So, what am I going to do with them? Why do you have your big, sharp teeth out? Please don't *eat* me! I will give you the milk and cookies if you don't eat me ... *argh!*

Gobble, gobble, gobble, gulp!

When I fell down into the wolf's stomach, I saw my gran there. I shouted, 'You monster! How could you eat a sweet gran like her? You monster! You monster!'

I heard a voice. It was my dad, I think. Me and my gran shouted for help. My dad picked up the wolf and shook him up and down. First my gran fell out of the wolf's mouth. *Aha,* I thought. Something went wrong because everything went silent. But nothing was wrong, it was fine. Then I fell out of the wolf's mouth.

My dad chopped the wolf up into quarters and we all skipped home happily (except the wolf, of course). We had a big dinner when we got home. Do you know what it was? I do. *It was the wolf!*

Colette Sinclair (10)
Laurieston Primary School, Falkirk

Letter To Sleeping Beauty

Your Sleepiness,
Eternity Palace,
Dreamville,
Fairyland.

Dear Your Sleepiness,

I am writing to you after a brief encounter with a young girl (a member of the Muffet family as a matter of fact). I was nearly drowned by a bowl of warm porridge after having her throw it at me as she started to retreat.

If possible, I think you should do something about this (please), by contacting the RSSS, or should I say The Royal Society of Safety to Spiders. I value Your Sleepiness highly, but could you please venture a little deeper into this matter because my family and I are in immediate danger.

Yours silkily and stressfully,

Mr W E Bell (loyal member of the RSSS).

Toni Harding (11)
Llanybydder Primary School, Llanybydder

Jack And The Beanstalk

When Jack took the golden lyre, the ogre chased him down the beanstalk. Jack got to the bottom and began to chop the beanstalk down, but he wasn't quick enough. The ogre climbed down the beanstalk and stood glaring at Jack. Jack ran as fast as he could to get the lyre from his house. The lyre sang the ogre a lullaby to sing him to sleep. Jack ran to get help from the strongest people in the land. Everyone tied their ropes together. They tied them around the ogre's arms, legs and waist. They pulled him underneath the beanstalk. Jack climbed back up the beanstalk and asked the ogre's servants to knock the beanstalk down.

The servants killed the ogre and they celebrated in Jack's incredible, newly built cottage.

Thomas Crudge (8)
St Joseph's RC Cathedral Junior School, Swansea

Jack And The Beanstalk

When Jack took the golden lyre, the ogre chased him down the beanstalk. Jack got to the bottom and began to chop the beanstalk down, but he wasn't quick enough. The ogre climbed down the beanstalk and stood glaring at Jack.

Jack ran into the house to get some help. The beanstalk fell on the ogre and it was heavy enough to stop the ogre for one minute.

The ogre got up and crushed the beanstalk. He was very, very mad with Jack. The ogre ran after Jack but he tripped over a rock. The ogre stamped his foot and said, 'I nearly got you, Jack.'

The ogre destroyed the town. Everyone ran away.

Leanne Gronert (8)
St Joseph's RC Cathedral Junior School, Swansea

The Spider

I awoke one morning and saw a spider in my bedroom. I screamed and screamed until the spider went deaf. I ran and ran as fast as I possibly could. My mummy and daddy heard me scream and my daddy came and whacked the spider with a magazine.

Rhiannon Garrett (9)
St Joseph's RC Cathedral Junior School, Swansea

The Mysterious Dog

I woke up with a mysterious 'woof'. I looked under my bed. I saw two googley eyes staring at me. It popped out and I screamed. The room vibrated. It was a little tiny puppy about 10cms tall. It started talking to me. I said hello to the dog and it barked.

Jessica Morgans (9)
St Joseph's RC Cathedral Junior School, Swansea

Smelly Cheese!

I went into a cupboard to find something to eat. Suddenly, the fridge opened and a huge cheese hopped out! It had a terrible odour, like a skunk. I felt very green, just whiffing it. I felt like I was going to vomit any second. I fainted on the floor.

Megan Williams (9)
St Joseph's RC Cathedral Junior School, Swansea

The Walking, Talking Shoes

One morning there was a strange banging coming from upstairs. I went to have a look. When I approached my bedroom, the banging stopped. I went in and in my drawer there was a pair of walking, talking shoes. They were singing when suddenly I awoke, I was dreaming.

Francesca Combe (9)
St Joseph's RC Cathedral Junior School, Swansea

A Creature In The Zoo

I heard this weird noise coming out of a pen. It sounded like *moo-woof*, it was a weird noise alright.

When a zookeeper went in to feed the creature, he never came out. Oh no, I saw it. It has half cow and half dog. It was sick. *Boom, boom!*

Oliver Hughes (9)
St Joseph's RC Cathedral Junior School, Swansea

Unlucky

I awoke to the mysterious sound from my rusty, creepy cupboard. Suddenly, bits of bread were springing out of the cupboard. The cobwebs were rustling. The cupboard flew open and this hamster started nibbling on my nose. He ran away and jumped in the fridge. Then it went *boom!*

Lewis Towell (9)
St Joseph's RC Cathedral Junior School, Swansea

Jack And The Beanstalk

When Jack took the golden lyre, the ogre chased him down the beanstalk. Jack got to the bottom and began to chop the beanstalk down, but he wasn't quick enough. The ogre climbed down the beanstalk and stood glaring at Jack.

Jack was worried because he did not know what to do. He ran into the house so he could think what to do.

He got the lyre to sing the ogre to sleep. When the ogre was asleep, Jack thought he'd get the strongest people to kill the ogre. When Jack had found them, the ogre stirred but all of them hid away from him.

The ogre woke up and tried to find the people, but he could not because they crept quietly. When the ogre was awake, Jack found a unicorn with magic who killed the ogre and the ogre was never seen again.

Bryony Avo
St Joseph's RC Cathedral Junior School, Swansea

Witch's Spell

'Come on Selena, think of a spell. I wonder which one. Let's look through my spell book. Ah, here's one!'

'Whistle, banana, numble, bumble,
Shake with my wand to make it humble.
A bit of lemon to sweeten it up,
She will never know what I have made up.
Revenge on Snow White, this is all for her,
Snow White will fall to the floor in a blur.'

'Ah, that'll do the trick. Now for revenge. Snow White here I come!'

Shauna McCabe (10)
St Joseph's RC Cathedral Junior School, Swansea

Snow White

'Now then, what can I put in this apple? Ah! The book for poisonous spells, brilliant! Now then … a leg of a spider, an ear of a dog, the tail of a fish and the eye of a frog. I have added that. Next … the dust of a star, the wax of a candle and all of the other things I pick at random.'

The old hag was mixing and adding all of the things she wanted to put in to make it yucky.

Snow White was cleaning up the cottage since the dwarves had made a mess of it at dinner. Suddenly, there was a knock on the door. Snow White went to answer it and there stood an old hag and a pirate called Captain Crook. The old hag carried a basket of apples. Snow White took one and munched on it. She munched and munched and munched. Nothing happened. The hag took one, confused. She munched and died! Hip hip hooray! The witch was dead!

Annabel Bass (8)
St Joseph's RC Cathedral Junior School, Swansea

My Mini Saga

I nervously crept into a terrifying, suffocating closet with spiderwebs in each corner. Suddenly, *splat!* Gooey goo dripped on the poor, one-eyed, frightened robot. I picked up the stinky, gooey goo and threw it at the wall. *Bang!*

Calum Palla (9)
St Joseph's RC Cathedral Junior School, Swansea

Bob's Big Day

It was a breezy, bright day on the motionless, navy sea. Bob Wilkinson, an army man on the navy side, had a big job to do. It was 1939 and he had to blow the Germans out of the skies. He was aged 29, born on Wednesday, 12th July, 1910. He was chief plane watcher.

Crouched in his bunker, with his powerful gun, his hands began to shake. The day of his big battle had come. He was on the lookout for German planes. *Fire!* Down went a plane. They had a problem. No more missiles or bullets.

'Quick boys, give the Americans a shout!' bellowed Bob.

Down went the bombs on Germany. *Bang! Crash!* Germany was defeated. They had fought hard for six years. Bob knew that they couldn't have done it without a team effort.

John Dodd (9)
St Joseph's RC Cathedral Junior School, Swansea

The Monster Who Cried

I heard it in my closet banging on the door. I thought it was a cat. *Bang!*
The door opened and a monster ran up to me.

'No, please don't kill me!' I screamed. I put on a sad face.

It cried.

'I'm so sorry!'

Michaela Cardone-Randal (9)
St Joseph's RC Cathedral Junior School, Swansea

Send In The Clowns

One day when I was at the circus, there was a stupid clown. The clown stuffed himself into the cannon. He fired himself through a wall, hit an acid factory and landed in a pillow factory in a pile of pillows. Unluckily for him, they were about to demolish the building. The clown was no more. It was the most stupid thing I have seen in my entire life.

Kieran Harrington (10)
St Joseph's RC Cathedral Junior School, Swansea

Spooky Bears

All of a sudden my teddy opened its eyes. It came alive. I heard *crick, crick, crack* on the floor. It was coming closer. It was dribbling down my face. I peered at it. It climbed in bed. It was uncomfortable, so it started to bounce and growl. *Argh!*

Lucy Haigh (9)
St Joseph's RC Cathedral Junior School, Swansea

Dog

I heard a mysterious sound. The sound was barking, then clucking. I didn't live near any animals. I looked out of the window but saw nothing but trees. I heard the sounds again. There was nothing.

I heard tapping in the house. There stood a clucking dog. *Wow!*

Blessing Chanda (9)
St Joseph's RC Cathedral Junior School, Swansea

The Unknown Figure

Bang! I fell backwards. The unknown figure was laughing at me. I had goosepimples down my back and there was still a little creature there. I saw a pencil. I picked it up and threw it at the thing. It exploded goo everywhere.

Dylan Driscoll (10)
St Joseph's RC Cathedral Junior School, Swansea

Cinderella

Once upon a time there was an ugly stepsister. She knew she was ugly but her mum made her act like she was better than her beautiful stepsister. They made her wear rags to try and take her beauty away from her. Gabbriell felt sorry for her.

They named her Cinderella for she spent all her time cleaning the cinders. She did their washing and any other thing they needed doing. Gabbriell wanted to help her, but she was not allowed.

When they got an invitation to a ball, the evil stepmother made Gabbriell hide Cinderella's invitation. She hid it somewhere that she knew Buttons would find.

Cinderella helped the girls get dressed up for the ball. Gabbriell knew Cinderella had a beautiful ballgown that her mother had given to her.

Gabbriell left to go to the ball. She did not want to go because her life was already good. She did not want to meet a prince.

A strange girl walked into the palace. Gabbriell knew it was Cinderella, but pretended she didn't know. They danced till midnight and then she ran away.

Next day a page boy went round all the houses with a glass slipper. The prince said he would marry the girl that the shoe fitted. Every girl tried it on and when it came to Cinderella, it fitted. Gabbriell was so happy for her.

Vanessa Cavan
St Mary's RC Primary School, Bathgate

Snow White

'Oh, I wish I were as beautiful as the queen,' I said.

The queen was actually jealous of me and she had to know something, so she asked the magic mirror. 'Who is the fairest of them all?'

'Snow White is the fairest,' the mirror replied.

I was heading off into the woods and saw a cottage. It was really nice and it was decorated with flowers. I was desperate to see who lived there. I knocked and waited, but no one answered, so I went in.

I got really tired after I'd explored the house, so I went upstairs to go to sleep. There were seven beds and I laughed because they had silly names carved on them. I had a dream about me being the queen and it was the best dream I ever had.

Later on, men came in and they appeared to be seven dwarves. I had befriended them as I lived with them. The queen, whom I admired, was searching for me. When she found my location, she turned into an ugly old woman. She walked by the cottage one day while the dwarves were away. She gave me a delicious, red apple and I couldn't resist it. So I ate it, but it was a poisonous apple.

When the dwarves came back, they were shocked to find me lying on the floor! They put me in a coffin made out of glass.

Just then, a prince came and gave me a gentle peck on my lips and I woke up! He carried me away and we lived happily ever after!

Jacqueline Kerr
St Mary's RC Primary School, Bathgate

Cinderella - The Wedding

Today we hear some breaking news that the prince had found love. Cinderella lived with her stepmum and two ugly sisters. Cinderella's father died, so everything changed. Cinderella was not allowed to get expensive clothes or go out with her friends. Instead, she had to do the cleaning.

One of her sisters said, 'She does not deserve to be married to a prince'.

Cinderella said, 'All this would not have happened without my fairy godmother'.

Now married, she is looking forward to starting her own family and treating them the way she should have been.

Jamie Temperley
St Mary's RC Primary School, Bathgate

Cinders And The Disco

Once upon a time (well, sometime this year) there was a hip, funky girl named Cinders. Her father had died, so she lived with her stepmum and stepsisters, Hash and Bash. Hash and Bash were very, very mean. They made Cinders do all the housework.

While Cinders was doing the housework, King Dance-a-lot was organising a disco for his son, Prince Prance-a-lot. The king was hoping that the prince would meet his true love and they would dance all night. He sent all the invitations to all the single girls in the city.

When Cinders got her invite, she jumped for joy. Her stepmum said she could go if she had something to wear, but the only thing she could wear was her mum's old sixties outfit. She decided to customise it so it looked funky and up to date. It was the most amazing thing you've ever seen, but her sisters tore it to bits.

Cinders ran into the garden and cried. Then suddenly, her mother appeared and gave her the funkiest outfit on Earth. She also warned her that she had to be back home by two o'clock.

She went to the disco and had an amazing time. She danced with the prince all night until two. Cinders ran out of the disco, dropping her hair bobble. The prince ran after her, but he couldn't catch her, but he did find her bobble.

The next day he asked all the girls if it was theirs and when Cinders said it was hers, the prince knew for sure she was the one and surprisingly, they ended up going to college together.

Hollie Greenshields (10)
St Mary's RC Primary School, Bathgate

The Gingerbread Dude

Deep in the horrible wilderness, a witch was making something, something that smelled very good. All day the witch slaved and slaved until it was ready. She took the tray out of the oven and took a look at her creation. It was a gingerbread dude. She moved to grab the gingerbread dude when suddenly, it got up and ran, singing, 'Run, run, as fast as you can, you can't catch the gingerbread dude!'

The gingerbread dude ran out of the house and met a giant scorpion. He asked, 'What are you doing here all alone in the cruel wilderness?'

'I am running away,' replied the gingerbread dude.

The scorpion lunged at the gingerbread dude as he ran away singing, 'Run, run, as fast as you can, you can't catch the gingerbread dude!'

He ran and ran, then he bumped into a large dragon!

'Raaaaaaaaaaaaah!' roared the dragon.

'Arrrgggghhhh!' screamed the gingerbread dude.

A smile ran across the dragon's face. 'Do you need a hand getting across the river of lava?' asked the dragon.

'Well … yes,' said the gingerbread dude timidly.

'Get on my mouth so that I can catapult you over to the other side,' instructed the dragon.

The gingerbread dude did as he was told. He climbed onto the dragon's mouth and … *snap!* Poor gingerbread dude was no more as the dragon had just eaten him whole!

Mehdi Bel Abbes (11)
St Mary's RC Primary School, Bathgate

Let's Get Funky Missy B

Missy B, a funky girl, lived with her stepmum, stepbro and stepsis. She did all the housework on her own.

One day, a man invited Missy B's step-brother, stepsis and stepmum to a *massive* beach party. Missy B desperately wanted to go, but her stepmum wouldn't let her. Suddenly, Missy B had a great idea. She looked in the Yellow Pages and found a great ad. The ad was just perfect. It read: *Funky Ideas for Beach Parties.* Missy B gave them a ring. Once she told them what the problem was, they felt so sorry for her that they sent their best designer to meet her.

When the designer came, she gave Missy B a really funky bathing suit, fancy stilettos and a *really* hot ride. She also gave her a super cool chauffeur called Bingy. But there was one problem, by the end of the last song Missy B would return to her usual rags, the car would become an old Ford Escort and the chauffeur would become a geek.

When they got there, Missy B was immediately attracted to a young man. He turned round and was immediately attracted to Missy B. Suddenly the last song ended. Missy B hung her head sadly, waiting for the change, but it never came!

'Can I give you a ride home?' said the man.

When she got out her ride was still there. 'My limo is round here, I'll give you a lift,' she said.

Missy B and her cool man drove off into the sunset.

James Duffy
St Mary's RC Primary School, Bathgate

The Dark Side Of Goldilocks

We all know the story of Goldilocks and the three bears. This is how the bears say it happened:

'Well,' said Pa Bear.

Ted started to cry. 'Boo-hoo, she broke my chair, Dad!' he said.

'There, there,' Pa comforted Ted.

Ma Bear said, 'She wiped us clean out. A short girl came and asked us to help her round up her flock and we agreed. So we finished doing that and came home to find Goldilocks being carted off in a police van. Good riddance, I say.'

Jordan Burns (11)
St Mary's RC Primary School, Bathgate

The True Story Of Goldilocks

'Well,' Goldilocks said, 'I was walking through the woods when I saw a house. Now I had to pay off a debt for my new hair curls (laugh), so when I see a house that hopefully no one is in, I can't resist robbing the place! I always carry a balaclava with me anyway, so I was prepared.

I first knocked on the door to make sure no one was in, then I opened the door. I saw three bowls of porridge and I was so hungry that I ate them all! I was full. I went into the living room to try to steal the TV but whilst there, I broke a wooden seat (I leant the TV on it). But I was needing more stuff, so I went upstairs.

There were lots of shelves. I saw a wooden box on one of the shelves above a small bed. I tried to get it down but it fell on me! I fell onto the bed, unconscious.

When I awoke, I heard footsteps. I ran to hide in a cupboard but something tickled my neck. I screamed and ran out of the door all the way home.

Kayleigh Bidwell (12)
St Mary's RC Primary School, Bathgate

Cinderella

My name is Velda. I have a twin sister and I have a stepsister called Cinderella. My sister, mum and I hate her. She thinks she is perfect and can do what she wants. Well, she can't. Nobody gets what they want except me.

Cinderella's father died a long time ago. My mum was unfortunately left with her. She does all the cleaning.

We got a letter from the prince asking us if we would go to a ball. My sister and I were only invited because they didn't know that Cinderella existed. Cinderella was very upset that she wasn't going.

When we all left, a fairy godmother appeared to Cinderella. She said, 'You are going to that ball, so go and get me a pumpkin!' The fairy godmother turned the pumpkin into a carriage. She turned the horse into a coachman and the mice into horses. Then she said, 'Only one more thing,' and changed Cinderella's ragged dress into a beautiful ballgown.

Cinderella went and danced with the prince. She fell in love with him. But suddenly, the clock chimed 12 and she had to go. As she ran out of the palace, her glass slipper came off.

The next day the prince went to every house in the village to see whose foot the glass slipper fitted. They came to my house and I tried it on, but I had no luck. Neither did my sister. Then, as they were leaving, Cinderella came down the stairs. She tried the slipper on and I was very angry because it fitted her.

She married the prince and lived happily ever after. It wasn't fair, she didn't deserve that.

Caroline Burns
St Mary's RC Primary School, Bathgate

Peter Pan

Once upon a time in a faraway land, there was a fairy named Tinkerbell who lived with her boyfriend, Peter Pan and the Lost Boys in Neverland. Everybody thought that Tinkerbell was always small, but she was the same size as Peter.

When Peter brought Wendy to Neverland she became jealous of Tinkerbell. Wendy was always trying to get Peter away from her, but she always followed them.

After a couple of days, Captain Hook came and captured Wendy and the Lost Boys. Wendy sneaked into Captain Hook's room and found some potions. She took one of them and put it in her pocket.

Later, she slipped the potion into Tinkerbell's drink. It was a shrinking potion. She took the drink through to Tinkerbell and sat down. Suddenly, Tinkerbell said that she didn't feel too good and then she started shrinking. Wendy started to laugh and told her that she'd put a potion in her drink. Tinkerbell was cursing and swearing and she ended up the size of a pin!

Now you know the real reason why Tinkerbell is so small. Next time you hear a fairy tale, think what could be the truth.

Matthew Kean
St Mary's RC Primary School, Bathgate

Three Billy Goats Gruff

Dear Helpline,

I am a troll who lives in a nice meadow and I have no friends. One day I was sleeping under a bridge in the shade and I heard a clip-clop on top of the old stone bridge. I climbed up and a small goat was there. I asked him to come for tea and biscuits, but the goat got scared and asked to go and eat some grass. I agreed.

A bigger one came and I offered to play tig, but it just got scared and asked to go and eat some grass. I agreed.

Then a huge one came over. I said, 'Hello, I suppose you want some gra …'

It butted me into the river. Now I feel very left out, so can you please help me get some friends?

Yours faithfully,

The Troll.

Mark Shedden (11)
St Mary's RC Primary School, Bathgate

Witch's Spell

I like a few frogs' legs,
With some spiders too!
Not only frogs' legs,
Newts' eyes will do.
Cinderella is a pest!
Soon I will be the best!

Charlie Margett (9)
Ysgol Bryn Teg, Llanelli

Lonely Mrs Giant

Dear Mrs Giant,

I'm sorry I killed your husband. I had to chop the beanstalk down or he would have eaten me.

I was very poor before I climbed the beanstalk, but I am not anymore because I took your money, golden harp and your chicken.

Don't be too lonely, I hope you find a new husband. If you don't and you are still lonely, then perhaps I could build a giant house next to mine and we would be next-door neighbours.

From Jack.

Bethany Mullen (8)
Ysgol Bryn Teg, Llanelli

Letter To The Three Billy Goats Gruff

Dear Three Billy Goats Gruff,

    I have heard that you have been clattering across Mr Troll's house and disturbing him as he watches TV. As well as that, you have been going to the loo on his bridge and now, for doing that, we will put a big gate there to stop you Three Billy Goats Gruff from disturbing him.

    Yours sincerely,

    Katie Burton.

Katie Burton (10)
Ysgol Bryn Teg, Llanelli

Spell For Stig

Freshly made T-shirt,
New blue jogging trousers,
A hat for his head,
67 pairs of trainers.
Shades to protect his eyes from the sun
Stig will be the coolest guy in town!

Andrew Lloyd (10)
Ysgol Bryn Teg, Llanelli

Letter To Santa

Dear Santa,

I didn't mean to swap my sister's present, but she was rubbing it in that she was getting all of the Shelti books, so in the night I swopped the presents.

From Laura.

PS: Merry Christmas.

Laura Kenyon (11)
Ysgol Pentreuchaf, Pwllheli

My Letter To A Friend

Dear Angharad,

Would you like to come to the zoo with me on the 16th of July? My mum would come and pick you up at 9am. We could see the amazing lions, the waddling penguins and also the hilarious monkeys.

See you soon.

Elain.

Elain Lloyd (10)
Ysgol Pentreuchaf, Pwllheli

A Witch's Spell To Cheese Crackers

25 spiders
And a glass of cider,
Lots of old silk
And some stale milk.
Bogeys in bananas,
Slugs in some slime,
Rotten maggots in a rotten mango,
All inside a cheese cracker!

Sioned Roberts (11)
Ysgol Pentreuchaf, Pwllheli

A Letter From School

Dear Warsley Family,

This is very unfortunate news to tell you, but your son, Bernard, has been unmannerly since his brother left. All of us have been trying to help, but we came to the conclusion at the school that only you can help him.

Thank you.

Yours sincerely,

Mr C Hughes.

Ceiri Coker (11)
Ysgol Pentreuchaf, Pwllheli

Staff Letter

Dear Mr Handell,

I am ashamed and truly sorry to say that your son, William, is daunting in the school. He only concentrates when we do Gothic pictures. He actually paralyses pupils. He is like a puncture in our school and immoral, although he got straight As in his PE class.

Your sincerely,

Mr Tokka.

Billy Bagilhole (11)
Ysgol Pentreuchaf, Pwllheli

WWE

Dear John Cena,

Please don't hurt me tomorrow. I will let you win, I promise, and hurt myself as well as jump from the top of the cage.

Your fellow wrestler.

Ray Mysterio.

PS: Looking forward to winning the belt!

Jim Ellis (11)
Ysgol Pentreuchaf, Pwllheli

Letter

Dear Headmaster,

Johnny will not be in school today because he fell from his bed and broke his hand and foot last night. He will be away for two weeks.

Yours sincerely,

Mr & Mrs Blunderfoot.

PS: Johnny would give an arm and a foot to be with you in class.

Gethin Roberts (11)
Ysgol Pentreuchaf, Pwllheli

Witch's Potion

One frog's leg and a pinch of salt,
Two eyeballs and a metal bolt.
I'll kill that Ceri,
Using one red cherry,
Half a fish head and that is it.
She will end up dead after a bit.
That's my potion and forever it will be,
Taste it, it's tea …

Manon Hollywood (11)
Ysgol Pentreuchaf, Pwllheli

Helping

Dear Natalie,

   Thank you for saving my life. Without your help, my brother would have hit me with a ruler on my head. I did try to pay him back, but it didn't work because he is bigger. So that's why I have got a black eye, it's obvious how.

   See you,
   Rhian.

Rhian Jones (10)
Ysgol Pentreuchaf, Pwllheli

I Hate Shopping

Oh no! Not this again!

Two ounces of butter, 170g of flour, one tablespoon of sugar, eggs, marzipan, icing, chocolate sprinkles and mostly jam and cream. I hate to bake. All of this for a stupid cake! I hate shopping!

Daniel Roberts (11)
Ysgol Pentreuchaf, Pwllheli